★ ★
★ **Doctor** ★
★ **Dolittle** ★

RED FOX READ ALONE

Red Fox Read Alones are fab first readers! With funny stories and cool illustrations, reading's never been so much fun!

Based on the stories by
HUGH LOFTING
Retold by Charlie Sheppard

★ Doctor ★
★ Dolittle ★
Takes Charge ★

Illustrated by Sarah Wimperis

RED FOX

A Red Fox Book

Published by Random House Children's Books
20 Vauxhall Bridge Road, London SW1V 2SA

A division of The Random House Group Ltd
London Melbourne Sydney Auckland
Johannesburg and agencies throughout the world

Text based on *Doctor Dolittle's Circus*
Copyright, 1924, by Hugh Lofting
Copyright, 1952, by Josephine Lofting
Copyright, 1988, by Christopher Lofting

1 3 5 7 9 10 8 6 4 2

This Read Alone Novel first published in Great Britain
by Red Fox 2000

Printed and bound in Denmark by
Nørhaven A/S, Viborg

Papers used by Random House Group Ltd are natural,
recyclable products made from wood grown in sustainable forests.
The manufacturing processes conform to the
environmental regulations of the country of origins.

The Random House Group Limited Reg. No. 954009

www.randomhouse.co.uk

ISBN 0 09 940559 8

Contents

Exciting News

Once upon a time there was a doctor who lived lived in the little town of Puddleby-on-the-Marsh, and his name was John Dolittle. Doctor Dolittle was an animal doctor. In fact he was a very special animal doctor, because he was the only man in the world who could actually speak to animals in their own languages.

The Doctor loved all creatures and all creatures loved him, but he was especially fond of the little family of animals who lived with him. There was Dab-Dab the duck who was the Doctor's housekeeper. She cooked his favourite dinners and always made sure he was carrying a clean handkerchief. Too-Too the owl was very good at counting and looked after the Doctor's money. Then there was Gub-Gub, Doctor Dolittle's greedy pet pig, Jip his dog and Whitey, the Doctor's little white mouse.

But perhaps the strangest creature who lived with the Doctor was the pushmi-pullyu, a rare animal from Africa. He had a head at each end of his body and could eat with one while talking with the other.

Well one morning Gub-Gub the pig came rushing into the Doctor's study looking very excited indeed.

'Doctor, Doctor,' he shouted, 'Blossom's Circus has come to Grimbledon.'

Grimbledon was the next town to Puddleby. It had a large field which was often used for shows and fairs.

'How exciting,' said the Doctor putting down his newspaper. 'Call the others at once. It's about time we all had some fun. I think we should go to the circus tonight.'

'Oh, thank you,' said Gub-Gub. 'There'll be toffee apples and candyfloss and lots of other good things to eat . . .' and he hurried out.

Just then Too-Too flew into the room. 'I'm sorry, Doctor,' he said, 'but I couldn't help overhearing. I'm afraid we won't be able to go to the circus. I've just been counting our money and we only have enough left to last us a week. Looking after so many animals is very expensive. We've already had to sell the piano. I'm afraid if you don't make some money soon we won't be able to afford to eat.'

By now the rest of the animals were crowding in at the door. Doctor Dolittle told them Too-Too's bad news.

'Do you mean we can't go?' said Gub-Gub. 'Do you mean we can't have any toffee apples?'

'I'm afraid not,' said Doctor Dolittle.

Poor Gub-Gub began to cry.

'Oh do stop, blubbering,' said Jip. 'We can't go and that's an end to it. There are more important things to worry about than toffee apples.'

'Yes,' said Dab-Dab, 'like how we're all going to eat with no money.'

Gub-Gub began to sob even louder.

Just then the pushmi-pullyu poked both his heads round the door. 'What else do they have at this circus?' he asked.

'Oh lots of things,' said Gub-Gub. 'An elephant, a bearded lady, a tightrope walker . . .'

'Do they have any two-headed animals?' asked the pushmi-pullyu.

'Of course not,' said Jip. 'No one else has ever seen a two-headed creature before. No one knows you exist.'

'Do you think they'd pay to see me?' asked the pushmi-pullyu.

'Oh, yes,' said Dab-Dab. 'People would much rather see you than a silly bearded lady.'

'Then why don't I join the circus?' asked the pushmi-pullyu. 'People would pay to look at me and I could make lots of money for you all.'

All the animals thought this was a fantastic idea. But Doctor Dolittle shook his head. 'I can't allow that,' he said. 'What, send a dear friend, all round the country locked in a cage for people to stare at? Never! We'll manage somehow.'

But the pushmi-pullyu insisted. He nodded both his heads up and down, saying he would like to repay Doctor Dolittle for all his kindness.

Doctor Dolittle thanked the pushmi-pullyu but told him he could never let him go off on his own. 'You're far too shy to live with people you don't know,' he said.

'Then why don't you all come with me?' said the pushmi-pullyu. 'We could all live at the circus and you could make sure that the ringmaster looks after me and the other animals properly.'

'Joining the circus!' squealed Gub-Gub, 'It's my dream come true! Yippee!'

'First, I think we should have a chat with the ringmaster,' said the Doctor. 'I'll send a note and invite Mr Blossom over to meet our incredible two-headed friend. If he's a nice man then I'll discuss joining the circus. But I'm not making any promises!'

Doctor Dolittle
Makes a Deal

Late that night, when Grimbledon Circus had closed, Mr Blossom, the ringmaster, came to the Doctor's house in Puddleby. He was a fat man with smiley eyes and a very very loud voice.

'I've come to see this amazing creature,' he shouted. 'I hope you're not wasting my time with silly tricks.'

17

Doctor Dolittle picked up a lantern and took Mr Blossom outside where the pushmi-pullyu was grazing on the lawn.

When Mr Blossom saw the two-headed creature his eyes nearly popped out of his head. 'How much do you want for that animal?' he asked, following the Doctor back into the house.

'He's not for sale,' said the Doctor.

'Oh, come now,' said Mr Blossom. 'I'll give you twenty pounds for him.'

'No,' said the Doctor.

'Thirty pounds,' said Mr Blossom.

The Doctor shook his head.

'Forty pounds – fifty pounds,' boomed the ringmaster. Then he went up and up, offering prices that made the animals gasp in surprise.

'It's no use,' said the Doctor. 'You must either take me and the pushmi-pullyu, or neither.'

Well, Mr Blossom wanted the two-headed creature in his circus so much, that in the end he agreed to take the Doctor and all his animals as well as the pushmi-pullyu. He said he would give them a new wagon all to themselves and that the money they made would be divided equally between the Doctor and himself.

'I'll send a caravan for you in the morning,' he shouted. 'Good night!'

Doctor Dolittle Meets Beppo

The next morning the animals packed their cases and waited for the caravan to arrive. As it turned the corner, they all got very excited. It was a brightly painted red-and-yellow gypsy caravan, with windows and a door and a chimney.

The horse pulling it, though, looked very tired.

'I think you should have a rest before you take us all back to Grimbledon,' Doctor Dolittle said to the poor horse. 'Dab-Dab, go and get him a drink of water.'

The horse was very grateful. He stood in the shade and told the Doctor that his name was Beppo and that he had been working in the circus for thirty-five years. He was sick of it, he said.

Doctor Dolittle decided he would ask Mr Blossom to let Beppo retire and live in peace.

When Beppo felt rested enough, the other animals all scrambled inside the caravan and they set off. When they reached Grimbledon they found Mr Blossom waiting to welcome them.

He led them to their stand. Across the front of it was a sign:

THE PUSHMI-PULLYU!
Come and see The
MARVELLOUS TWO-HEADED ANIMAL
FROM
THE JUNGLES OF AFRICA

Then, to everyone's delight, Mr Blossom offered to show them around the rest of the circus and side shows. He took them to see the zoo first. It was a horrible place. Most of the animals seemed dirty and unhappy. The Doctor was very angry and wanted to shout at the ringmaster about it. But Jip whispered in his ear, 'Don't say anything yet, Doctor. Wait until the boss sees how valuable you are with animals, then you'll be able to do what you like with him. If you kick up a fuss now, we might lose our job. Then you won't be able to help at all.'

This struck John Dolittle as good advice. And so for the time being he whispered to the animals through the bars of their cages that soon he would try to help them.

The Amazing Pushmi-Pullyu

The next day, the pushmi-pullyu was put on show for the first time. He was very popular. No one had ever seen a two-headed animal before and lots of people queued up to pay their money and have a look at him. At first he was shy and kept hiding one of his heads under the straw. Then the people wouldn't believe he had two heads. So the Doctor asked him to try to keep both of them on show.

But some of the silly people, even when they could see the two heads, kept prodding the poor pushmi-pullyu with sticks to see if part of him was stuffed. While two naughty boys were doing this the pushmi-pullyu got very annoyed. He brought both his heads up at the same time and jabbed the boys in the legs with his horns. Then they knew for sure that he was real all over.

Although the pushmi-pullyu was very popular, the Doctor and Too-Too realised that it would take quite a while for them to earn enough to live on and leave the circus. Doctor Dolittle was sad about this because there were lots of things in the circus that he did not like and he wanted to go home. The things that worried him most were the  poor animals in the zoo. At the end of the first day he had gone back and talked to them. They were all very unhappy; their cages were too small and not cleaned properly, and they did not get enough exercise or food.

The Doctor was so angry he went to see the ringmaster and told him about all the things he thought ought to be changed. Mr Blossom listened quietly until Doctor Dolittle had finished and then he laughed.

'If I do all the things you want me to, Doctor, I might as well leave the circus!' he said. 'I'll be ruined. What, let my horses retire? Build bigger cages and clean them all day? Buy more food? Take the animals out for walks? You must be crazy! You don't know anything about

 running a circus. I've let you show the pushmi-pullyu in your own way, but I'm going to run the rest of it my way. Understand?'

Sad at heart, the Doctor left the ringmaster's caravan. On the steps of his own wagon he found Jip, chewing a bone. Nearby, Beppo was cropping the scrubby grass by the light of the moon.

'Nice night,' said Jip. 'You look kind of worried, Doctor. Anything wrong?'

'Yes,' said John Dolittle, sitting down miserably on the steps beside him. 'Everything's wrong. I've just been talking to Blossom about the zoo. He won't do a thing to help the animals.'

'But, Doctor,' said Jip. 'You've hardly begun. Don't worry.'

'It's no good, Jip. I'm not helping at all and I can't stay and see animals unhappy. I shouldn't have come here.'

At this moment Beppo, hearing his friend's voice, came closer.

'Hello, Beppo,' said John Dolittle. 'I'm afraid Mr Blossom won't listen to me so I think I am going to leave the circus.'

'But you're our one hope,' said the old horse. 'Be patient. You can't change everything in a minute. If you go, then we'll never get anything we want. But we know that if you stay, before long you will be running the whole show the way it should be run. Please stay.'

For a moment the Doctor was silent.

'Well,' said Jip. 'Are we going to stay?'

'Yes, Jip,' said the Doctor. 'I think we've got to.'

The Show Must Go On!

Mr Blossom had put big posters up all over the town telling everybody about the circus and the wonderful acts: Trapeze Artists; the Strongest Man on Earth; a Side-Splitting Clown; Jojo, the Dancing Elephant; and Nino, the World Famous Talking Horse.

Now this Nino was just an ordinary horse who had been trained by Mr Blossom to answer signals. He didn't really talk at all. When the ringmaster said, 'What's three plus four, Nino?' Nino would stamp the floor seven times. And if the answer was yes, he would nod his head up and down, and if it was no, he would shake it from side to side. He didn't understand the questions at all. When Mr Blossom wanted Nino to say yes, he would secretly scratch his left ear; when he wanted him to answer no, he would fold his arms.

The ringmaster didn't tell anyone the secret of all these signals, but, of course, the Doctor knew all about them because Nino had told him.

Well, one afternoon, just before the show in the big tent was about to begin, the Doctor and Mr Blossom were in the clown's dressing room talking. Suddenly in rushed the head stableman.

'Mr Blossom,' he shouted, 'Nino's sick! He's lying in his stable with his eyes closed. The show's due to begin in fifteen minutes and I can't get him to stand up.

Mr Blossom jumped up and rushed over to the stable, with the Doctor close behind him. When they got to Nino's stall, they found the horse in a bad way. The Doctor managed to get Nino to stand up, but after the poor horse had walked a few steps he became very weak and wobbly.

'Nino has a bad fever,' explained the Doctor.

'He won't be able to perform today. In fact he probably won't be well enough to perform for a week.' And he got some large pills out of his black bag and gave the horse two.

'He'll have to!' cried Mr Blossom. 'He's the star act. The audience will ask for its money back if he doesn't appear.'

At that moment a stable boy came up. 'We'll need you in the ring soon, Mr Blossom. The crowd is getting bigger.'

'We're ruined!' shouted the ringmaster, throwing up his hands in despair. 'If Nino doesn't go on, the crowd's going to ask for their money back. I haven't got anything to put in his place.'

Poor Mr Blossom was very upset. Just then Beppo, in the stall next to Nino's, neighed quietly. Doctor Dolittle started to smile.

'I think I can help you out of this trouble, Mr Blossom,' he said. 'But if I do you've got to promise me a few things. I know more about animals than you think, and I'm going to tell you a secret, which I don't boast about because nobody would believe me if I did. I can talk to horses in their own language.'

Doctor Dolittle's Secret

Blossom looked at John Dolittle and frowned. 'Are you crazy?' he said. 'Talk to animals in their own language! Look here, I've been in the circus thirty-seven years, and I know people can't speak to animals. You've got a cheek to tell me a story like that – me, Mr Blossom!'

'I am not telling you stories,' said the Doctor quietly. 'I am telling you the truth.'

'Prove it,' said Mr Blossom.

'Well, there are five horses in this stable, aren't there?' said the Doctor. 'And none of them can see me when I stand here, can they? Now if you will ask me to put some questions to any one of them I will give you his answer.'

'Oh, you're crazy!' said Mr Blossom. 'I haven't got time to fool with you.'

'All right,' said the Doctor. 'I was trying to help you, but if you don't want my help then there's nothing I can do.'

He shrugged his shoulders and turned away. The sound of clapping came from the big tent.

'Ask Beppo,' said Mr Blossom suddenly, 'to tap the number of the stall he's in.' Beppo's was the second from the end. On his door was marked a large '2' in white paint.

'All right,' said the Doctor. And he made some snuffly breathing noises. Immediately two taps sounded from stall number two.

Mr Blossom's eyebrows shot up in surprise. But then he shrugged his shoulders.

'Pshaw! That could easily have been an accident. Maybe he just fell against the partition. Ask him to pull down the rag hanging over his stable door and throw it up in the air.'

'All right,' said the Doctor. And he made some more snuffly noises, ending with a neigh. Suddenly the rag disappeared. The Doctor had not moved. Mr Blossom ran down the stable to look inside stall number two. There he found Beppo tossing the rag up in the air and catching it.

'Now do you believe me?' asked the Doctor.

'Believe you!' cried Mr Blossom. 'I believe you're the man I want, all right. Come on down to the dressing room and let's put some clothes on you.'

'What do you mean?' asked the Doctor.

'Dress you up, of course, ready for your act,' said Mr Blossom. 'You said you were going to help me?'

'Yes,' answered John Dolittle slowly, 'and I will – after you have promised me a few things'.

'I'll promise you anything,' cried Mr Blossom. 'If you can talk animals' language we'll make a fortune! Come on over and we'll pick you out some fancy clothes.'

Blossom and the Doctor made their way across to the dressing rooms, where the ringmaster began pulling costumes out of some trunks. While the ringmaster went through the brightly coloured clothes, the Doctor told him what he wanted in return for giving the performance.

'Now, Mr Blossom,' he said, 'ever since I joined your circus I have been very upset by the way you treat your animals. I have tried to talk to you about this before but you won't listen to me.'

'I'm very sorry,' said Mr Blossom. 'Tell me what you want and I'll do my

best to help.'

'Well for a start,' said the Doctor, 'Beppo, the horse I will use for the talking act, is far too old to work. I want him to be allowed to retire for the rest of his days.'

'I agree,' said Mr Blossom. 'Now how would this do?' He held up a bright yellow waistcoat against the Doctor's chest. 'No, too small.'

'I also want you to be kinder to your other animals,' said Doctor Dolittle.

'All right, Doc, I'll do anything you ask. Why don't you write out some rules and I'll stick to them. Oh my! Here's the very thing. Just your size.'

Mr Blossom held up a bright scarlet tunic. 'Ever seen anything so smart?' he chuckled.

At that moment the door opened and the stable boy came in.

'Joe, you're just in time,' said Mr. Blossom. 'Run over to the stables and brush down Beppo. He's going to do an act.'

'Beppo!' cried the boy in surprise.

'That's what I said!' shouted Mr. Blossom. 'And put the green halter on him with the white rosettes – and plait his tail with a red ribbon. Hop about it!'

The boy ran off to the stables as fast as he could.

'Now I'd better get out there and start the show,' said Mr Blossom buttoning up his ringmaster's jacket. 'Good luck, Doctor, and thank you for all your help.'

He shut the door behind him leaving the Doctor to finish putting on his costume.

When Doctor Dolittle was ready, Dab-Dab came in carrying a cup of tea for him. 'We've just heard about your act,' she said. 'I've brought you this to calm your nerves. My, you do look very smart, Doctor.'

'Thank you,' said the Doctor. 'I'm ever so excited. And guess what! Mr Blossom has agreed to take better care of all his other animals.'

'I knew you could do it,' said Dab-Dab.

There was another knock at the door and Gub-Gub came in munching his fifth toffee apple of the day. 'Only five minutes before the last act goes on, Doctor.'

'I'm nearly ready,' said the Doctor. 'Pass my hat, Dab-Dab. How's the crowd, Gub-Gub?'

'Great!' said the pig. 'It's the biggest audience the circus has had this year.'

The Greatest Show on Earth

'I think I'd better go and fetch Beppo now,' said Doctor Dolittle. As he opened the dressing room door, he heard the sound of cheers and clapping. 'Listen to that,' he said. 'Imagine how much they'll clap when they see Beppo. He's going to be the greatest act ever.'

Then the Doctor, dressed in his wonderful uniform, ran out of the dressing room to join his partner.

Poor Beppo did not look nearly as smart as the Doctor. His coat was long and his mane was straggly. Despite the green halter and the red ribbon in his plaited tail, he still looked very old and untidy.

'Oh, Beppo!' the Doctor murmured in his ear. 'Anyone would think you were going to a funeral. Cheer up! Hold your head up. That's it. Now blow out your nostrils . . . Ah much better!'

'Should we rehearse this act a bit first?' asked Beppo. 'I don't know what you want me to do.'

'No, we haven't got time now,' said John Dolittle. 'We'll have to be on stage any minute. But we'll manage. Just do everything I tell you. Look out, you're drooping your head again. Chin up! Arch your neck. That's the style! Now you look great.'

Jojo the dancing elephant had finished his act, and everybody was clapping. Mr Blossom walked into the centre of the ring and with a lordly wave of his hand, he silenced the band which was finishing Jojo's last dance.

'Ladies and gentlemen,' he roared at the sea of faces, 'we have now arrived at the last and most important act in our programme. Nino, the world-famous talking horse, and his owner, Captain Pufftupski. There they are, ladies and gentlemen – you see them before you in the flesh. Kings and queens have travelled miles to see their act.'

'Oh, stop this nonsense, Blossom,' whispered the Doctor looking very embarrassed. 'There's no need to . . .'

But the ringmaster hurried on in a loud voice: 'As for Nino, this clever horse can actually talk to his master. If you don't believe what I say, you can prove it for yourselves. All you have to do is to ask him a question through his owner and it will be answered. Captain Pufftupski and Nino will start their act with a few tricks just to show you what they can do. Ladies and gentlemen, I give you Captain Pufftupski, and his horse, the one and only, world-famous NINO.'

As the band played a little tune, the Doctor and Beppo stepped forward to the centre of the ring and bowed. The people clapped loudly.

It was a wonderful performance. The Doctor, when he entered the ring, had no idea of what he was going to do. Neither had Beppo. Every once in a while the old horse would forget to raise his head and slump back into his usual worn-out appearance. But on the whole, as Too-Too said afterwards, he made a much better-looking show horse than anyone had expected; and so far as the audience was concerned, he was the best act they had ever seen.

After doing a few amazing tricks, Doctor Dolittle turned to the people in the audience and offered to make the horse do anything they asked. Immediately a little boy in the front row cried out, 'Tell him to take my hat off.'

The Doctor made a sign or two
and Beppo went straight to the boy,
lifted the cap from his head and
put it into his hand. Then lots of

questions were shouted by the audience, and to every one Beppo gave an answer – sometimes by tapping the floor, sometimes by shaking his head, and sometimes by word of mouth, which the Doctor translated. The people enjoyed it so much that Mr Blossom thought they'd never finish. And when at last Captain Pufftupski led his horse out of the ring, the audience clapped and cheered and clapped and cheered.

The news of the wonderful talking horse quickly spread through the town. Long before the evening show was due, people were lining up outside the big tent, four deep, waiting patiently to get a seat. The rest of the field and all the side shows were packed so tight you could hardly move through the crowds.

Beppo's Decision

All these extra people meant there were soon enormous crowds to see the pushmi-pullyu as well. After a few hours Doctor Dolittle's money box was very full.

'I think,' said Too-Too, putting his mathematical head on one side, 'that if things carry on like this, in six days we should have made enough money to leave the circus and go back home.'

'And most of that you can put down to the Doctor's act with Beppo,' said Jip. 'If it wasn't for that act, and the talk it has made, the crowds wouldn't be half as big.'

When Mr Blossom saw what a success Doctor Dolittle and Beppo had been, he begged the Doctor to do the act again that night and for another week.

'But I've promised Beppo that he can retire for helping you out in your emergency,' said the Doctor. 'I didn't say anything to him about acting all week.'

'But the news of this amazing show has spread all over the town,' said Mr Blossom, 'and a long way outside of it, too. People are coming from miles around to see your act. Can't you ask Beppo to help us? Tell him I'll give him anything he likes – asparagus for breakfast and a feather bed to sleep in! My circus is taking in hundreds of pounds a day now. If this keeps up I shall be able to retire myself soon.'

Doctor Dolittle looked very angry and he paused a moment before he answered.

'Oh, yes,' he said rather sadly, 'you're only being nice to him now that he is making you money. For years he has worked for you and you've never even brushed his coat in return. Now you'll give him anything in the world. Money! Bah!'

'Well,' said Blossom, 'I'm helping to make up for it now, aren't I? It isn't hard work, answering questions and doing tricks. Please go and talk to him, Doctor.'

'All right, I'll ask him and see what he says. But remember, if he says no you must still give him what you promised – a comfortable home for the rest of his life.'

The Doctor found Beppo gazing out of the window of his stall.

'Is that you, John Dolittle?' he said, as the Doctor opened the door. 'Have you come to take me away?'

'Beppo,' said Doctor Dolittle, putting his hand on the horse's bony back, 'you're famous.'

'How's that, Doctor? I don't understand.'

'Mr Blossom has just found out how valuable you are because you can talk.'

'But I've always talked.'

'Yes, I know. But Mr Blossom didn't know that until I proved it to him in the circus ring. Now, he doesn't want you to retire. He wants you to keep talking, the way you've always done.'

'It sounds crazy, doesn't it, Doctor?'

'Very. But you have suddenly become so valuable to him that he will give you asparagus for breakfast and a servant to brush your coat if you'll stay and act for him for another week.'

'Humph! That's what it means to be famous, does it? I'd rather graze in a nice big field.'

'Well, Beppo, you are to suit yourself. I've told Blossom I'm going to hold him to his promise. If you don't want to do it, say so. You can retire today if you want.'

'What do you think I should do, Doctor?'

'The only thing is,' said Doctor Dolittle, 'that if you and I give Mr Blossom what he wants now, he may earn enough money to help all the other animals as well.'

'All right, Doctor,' said Beppo. 'Then that settles it. I'll do it.'

Mr Blossom was the happiest man on earth when John Dolittle told him that Beppo had agreed to act for another week.

He at once got posters printed which said that the world-famous talking horse was to be seen at Grimbledon for only one more week, and that those who did not wish to miss the chance of a lifetime had better hurry up and come to Blossom's Circus.

Mr Blossom
Makes Some Changes

In the next few days, Mr Blossom
did what he'd promised and started
to take better care of his animals.
Doctor Dolittle gave him a list of
rules which he had to follow. The
carpenters were sent for and every
animal was built a bigger cage with
special drainage underneath to keep
it warm and dry. The Doctor told Mr
Blossom that these cages would
have to be cleaned out twice a day.

Then John Dolittle made the

ringmaster order up all the special
foods that the animals wanted,
like currant buns
for the elephant

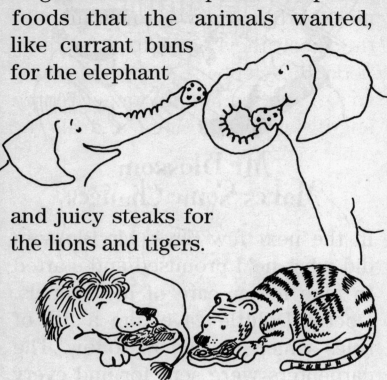

and juicy steaks for
the lions and tigers.

A few weeks before, of course,
the ringmaster would not have spent
so much on his animals. But now,
with John Dolittle bringing him in
lots of money, he was ready to do
anything to please him.

The thing was, however, that the nicer Mr Blossom was to his animals, the nicer they were back to him. Soon the elephant stopped looking so sad and the lion no longer roared angrily at Mr Blossom and all the other visitors.

'Do you know, Doctor,' said Mr Blossom towards the end of the week, 'I'm actually enjoying my job more now that the animals are happier. They're much nicer to me in the ring and lots of children are coming back again and again just to see Mr Blossom's "happy" animals.'

'I'm very glad to hear it,' said the Doctor.

'And did you know that the tigers like having their heads scratched? I discovered that this morning. They actually started to purr when I did it.'

Of course Doctor Dolittle knew, but he didn't say so.

By the end of the week, John Dolittle and Mr Blossom had made more money than they could ever have imagined. They arranged that after the last performance on Saturday, the Doctor and his animals would take Beppo to live with a farmer who had agreed to look after the old horse for the rest of his life. Afterwards the Doctor and his pets would make their way back to Puddleby and leave the circus for good. They'd made enough money to live well for a long time, and the Doctor wanted to start looking after sick animals again.

Farewell to the Circus

The last performance was over and Beppo, Doctor Dolittle and his pets were all ready to leave. Mr Blossom and most of the circus animals walked them to the circus gates to say good-bye.

'I'm really going to miss you all,' said Mr Blossom. 'But don't worry, I've learned my lesson and I'm going to treat my animals much better from now on.'

'I know,' said the Doctor, watching the lions lying happily at Mr Blossom's feet.

'As for you, Beppo,' said the ring-master, patting the old horse's head, 'I'm very sorry that I treated you so badly for all those years. I know it won't make up for all I've done, but I've bought you a little present.'
He handed a parcel to the Doctor. Inside was a beautiful sky-blue blanket. 'This should keep you warm in the winter,' he said, and Beppo nuzzled Mr Blossom to show him how much he liked it.

Then Doctor Dolittle led his animals out of the circus towards Beppo's new farm.

After a while Dab-Dab, who was riding some of the way on the horse's back, said, 'What do you think your new home will be like, Beppo?'

'The place I've always dreamed of,' said Beppo, 'would have big trees to stand under, and a stream which is always sparkling and clear. It would have a nice shelter with a roof that doesn't let the rain in. It would have long hay-grass with buttercups.

And in the middle of the field there would be a scratching post so that I could scratch my neck as the sun goes down.'

'It sounds lovely,' said the Doctor. 'Almost like the place where I'd wish to spend my own old age – though I suppose I'd want a little more furniture than a scratching post.'

At last they came to the little red-roofed farm which Mr Blossom had told them about.

'Now, remember, Beppo,' said Doctor Dolittle, 'if you're not happy here, then Mr Blossom will find you somewhere else.'

Doctor Dolittle knocked on the farm door and a jolly farmer's wife popped her head out of an upstairs window. 'Doctor Dolittle,' she said.

'My husband's been expecting you. He's in the shed milking the cows. Let him know you're here and he'll show you the field we've got ready for your horse.'

Doctor Dolittle found the farmer who led them into the loveliest meadow you ever saw. It was almost as if some fairy had made old Beppo's wish come true, because it was the home he had described in every detail.

'This is it, Doctor,' said Beppo quietly. 'This is the spot – just as I had always imagined it. No horse could ask for a better place to pass his old age.'

'It's wonderful,' said the Doctor. 'I hope you'll be very happy here.'

After the Doctor and the other animals had said good-bye to Beppo, the farmer invited them into his house for a glass of lemonade.

'That's very kind of you,' said the Doctor, 'but we must get going. It's a long way home and we don't want to be travelling in the dark.'

So the Doctor and his animal family turned towards the setting sun and started for home. As they got to the top of the hill they looked back and saw Beppo prancing around in his new meadow.

'Oh look at him,' said Dab-Dab. 'He's so happy thanks to you, Doctor.'

'And so are all the other animals at the circus,' pointed out Jip.

Doctor Doctor smiled and patted Gub-Gub's head. 'I hope you're right,' he said. 'I hope you're right.' And with happy hearts, he and his animal family walked home to Puddleby.